activity

Crossword

The be-bop bugs love to be outside when the sun is shining.
Debbie Dragonfly and her friends have so much fun playing by the stream.
Use the picture below to find the answers to the questions in the crossword.

Across

1. Which bug can you see that makes honey?
2. Which bug has big blue wings?
3. What have the ants made from a leaf?
4. What is Lucy Ladybug sitting on?

Down

1. What color are Lucy Ladybug's spots?
3. Which bug is building a web?
4. What does Debbie Dragonfly use to fly?
5. What is Benny Bee sitting on?

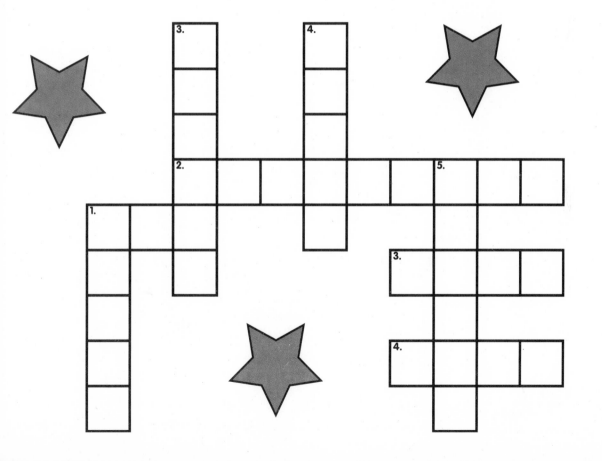

Find-a-Word

The be-bop bugs enjoy fun times in the land of Happy Bugs.
The words below are hidden in the find-a-word.
See if you can find the words by looking across and down.

| Grasshopper | Petal | Ladybug | Pond | Dragonfly |
| Caterpillar | Flowers | Tree | Leaf | Ant |

C	A	T	E	R	P	I	L	L	A	R
D	F	Q	T	O	W	D	A	G	N	Y
R	U	F	L	L	T	Y	D	L	T	P
A	K	H	E	S	R	X	Y	V	C	E
G	V	S	A	A	E	D	B	M	T	T
O	C	D	F	K	E	Q	U	V	N	A
N	A	P	P	O	N	D	G	I	C	L
F	Z	U	T	I	D	H	Z	M	O	F
L	L	T	Y	F	L	O	W	E	R	S
Y	W	Q	F	T	V	B	F	J	L	E
G	R	A	S	S	H	O	P	P	E	R

Missing Letters

Andy, Amelia and Artie Ant watch as Bella crawls out of
her cocoon as a beautiful butterfly.

Fill in the missing letters to complete the words below.

B☐TTE☐FLY

C☐CO☐N

A☐T

C☐AWLS

Maze

Benny Bee and his friends are
tired after spending the
day playing in the flowers.
Help them to find their way
back to their hive.

START

FINISH

Dot-to-Dot

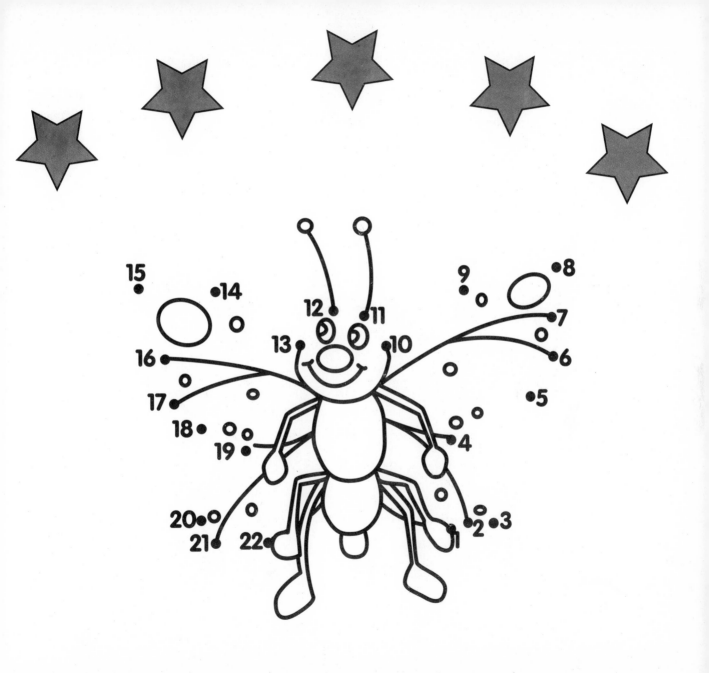

Match the Clues

Can you match the clues opposite to the bugs on this page?

1

I like to jump around.
I like to hide in the grass.
I am green.
WHO AM I?

2

I live in a hive.
I like to make honey.
I am yellow and black.
WHO AM I?

3

feed on pollen from flowers.
have beautiful bright wings.
love to fly around the garden.
WHO AM I?

4

I love eating green leaves.
I move very slowly.
I have many legs.
WHO AM I?

5

I have eight long legs.
I make a web.
I love to eat flies.
WHO AM I?

Questions & Answers

Frankie Fly and Bernie Bug are good friends, they love to play in the garden.
Look very hard at the picture of Frankie and Bernie to see if
you can answer the questions on the opposite page.

How many petals on the yellow flower?

 **What part of Frankie Fly is bright red?**

 **How many legs does Bernie have?**

 How many purple flowers can you see?

Spot the Difference

Can you spot the four differences between the two pictures of
Artie Ant and Clancy Caterpillar?

a.

b.

1

Can you spot the four differences between the
two pictures of Lucy Ladybug?

a.

b.

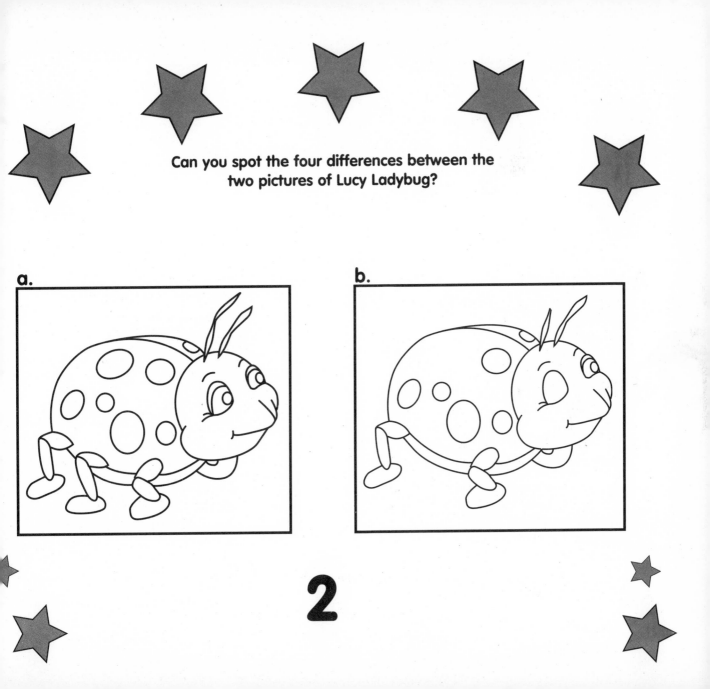

2

Solutions

Crossword

		S				W						
		P				I						
		I				N						
		D	R	A	G	O	N	F	L	Y		
B	E	E	R			S			L			
L		R					B	O	A	T		
A								W				
C						L	E	A	F			
K								R				

Find-a-Word

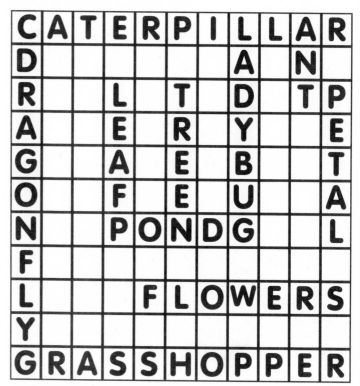

Missing Letters

BUTTERFLY
COCOON
ANT
CRAWLS

Maze

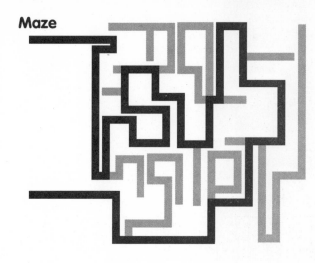

Dot-to-Dot

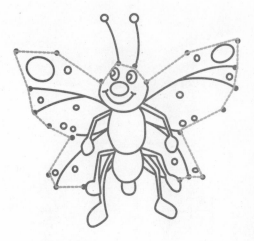

Match the Clues

1. Grasshopper 2. Bee 3. Butterfly 4. Caterpillar 5. Spider

Questions & Answers

1. Six 2. Nose 3. Six 4. Two

Spot the Difference

Image 1:b
- one of caterpillar's antennae is missing
- one of ant's arms is missing
- one of ant's eyes is closed
- caterpillar is missing a spot

Image 2:b
- one spot is missing
- half of an antenna is missing
- one leg is missing
- one eye is shut

This edition published and distributed by
THE BOOK COMPANY PUBLISHING PTY LIMITED
Austlink Corporate Park, 1 Minna Close
Belrose Sydney NSW 2085 Australia
sales@thebookcompany.com.au

© 2003 The Book Company Publishing Pty Limited

Publisher: Glenn Johnstone
Production: Leslie Krey & Mary Bjelobrk

Printed in China